A Director's Guide

The future of communications for business

UNDERSTANDING AND EXPLOITING CHANGES IN VOICE AND DATA TECHNOLOGY

Editor, Director Publications: Tom Nash
Managing Editor: Lesley Shutte
Consultant Editor: Marc Beishon
Production Manager: Victoria Davies
Design: Halo Design
Commercial Director: Simon Seward
Managing Director: Andrew Main Wilson
Chairman: George Cox

Published for the Institute of Directors
and Cable & Wireless Communications
by Director Publications Ltd
116 Pall Mall London SW1Y 5ED

Editorial: 020 7766 8910
Production: 020 7766 8960
Sponsorship: 020 7766 8885
Copy sales: 020 7766 8766
Facsimile: 020 7766 8990

YOURS TO HAVE AND TO HOLD
BUT NOT TO COPY

Director Publications Ltd
116 Pall Mall
London SW1Y 5ED

Kogan Page Ltd
120 Pentonville Road
London N1 9JN

©Director Publications Ltd 2000

British Library Cataloguing in Publication Data
A CIP record for this book is available from the British Library
ISBN 0 7494 3378 7

Printed and bound in Great Britain

Contents

INTRODUCTION **Demystifying today's technologies** 5
George Cox, Director General, IoD

FOREWORD **Taking a look behind the predictions** 7
Rob Fisher, Chief Executive,
Cable & Wireless Communications

1 **Communicating for success** 9
Marc Beishon, business and technology writer

2 **The new models for business** 14
Rob Fisher, chief executive, Cable & Wireless Communications

3 **The e-business imperative** 19
Marc Beishon, business and technology writer

4 **The workplace of the 21st century** 24
Wes McGregor, director of Advanced Workplace Associates

5 **Communications for customer service** 31
Stephen Morrell, consultant at marketing analysts Datamonitor

6 **Voice and data integration** 37
Stuart Keeping, product director, IP Applications,
Cable & Wireless Communications

7 **The third mobile revolution** 44
Frank Williams, business and technology writer

8 **The practical applications of convergence** 49
Nick Langley, business and technology writer

9 **Strategies for competitive advantage** 55
David Jackson, director of voice services,
Cable & Wireless Communications

10 **All for one, one for all** 61
Philip Hunter, technology writer

11 **Choosing a service provider** 67
Annie Gurton, business and technology writer

Daily, we carry nearly one third of all the world's Internet traffic.

CABLE & WIRELESS

Demystifying today's technologies

George Cox, Director General,
Institute of Directors

People have been talking of "convergence" – the coming together of IT, telecommunications and the media – for about 25 years. We saw its first effects with the impact of computer technology on telephony: a step which transformed an industry which had been largely moribund for the previous three-quarters of a century. However, that was only the start. We are now beginning to see more of the real, long-predicted, impact.

Today's businesses are interested in seeing, combining and exchanging information in a variety of forms: the printed word, facts and figures, video, voice and high-quality graphics. They are looking to expand and enhance their activities on the internet, and to establish faster and more efficient means of communication both within their own organisations and with other businesses and customers. The tools for doing so are fast becoming available.

Advances in technology, liberalisation of the market and a massive increase in competition are driving prices down and broadening choice. This offers enormous potential for those businesses that equip themselves rapidly to exploit these new opportunities.

However, it is all too easy to be overwhelmed by the burgeoning range of technologies. New devices, new facilities, new services become available by the day. This guide, therefore, sets out to demystify the choice available to today's business, and to outline the key developments and their implications.

Is your network ready for e-business?

Business Made Simpler

CABLE & WIRELESS

Taking a look behind the predictions

Rob Fisher, Chief Executive, Cable & Wireless Communications

No business presentation would be complete without the presence of an upward-sloping graph pointing to an assured corporate future. Whether predicting sales, revenue or turnover, the future in these scenarios always seems more secure than the present.

The introduction of the internet into the business process has transformed the upward-sloping curve into an art form. Current predictions range from the spread of call centres (a quarter of the UK workforce will work in call centres by 2002), to the number of internet users worldwide (400m by the same year).

Unlike the predictions of the past, however, these upward-sloping curves are not a guarantee of security and prosperity. In tomorrow's marketplace, the businesses that survive and prosper will be those which adapt to the opportunities presented by new technology. Traditional channels to market are being complemented and, in some cases usurped, by new channels such as the telephone, the internet, interactive television and mobile phones.

In this Director's Guide, produced in conjunction with Cable & Wireless Communications, we aim to look behind the predictions at the impact that concepts such as e-commerce and computer telephony integration are likely to exert on the workplace, and how businesses can prepare themselves for this evolving environment.

In contrast to the business trends of the past such as privatisation of the 1980s and globalisation of the 1990s, the move towards e-commerce has been driven as much by consumers as any other political or economic factors. Customers themselves are determining their own preferred channels to vendors, and measuring quality of service on the ability to deliver across all these channels consistently. In many instances, the ability to deliver products across a range of media has become more important than the product itself.

Since I began this foreword with a reference to the bold upward-sloping predictors of yesteryear, it seems appropriate to return to them. As Thomas Watson, one-time chairman of IBM and author of technology's most famously wayward prediction that there would be a total world market for "about five computers" would testify, hindsight is indeed a wonderful thing. IBM went onto to become the largest computer manufacturer the world has ever known – long live the bold, upward-sloping bar chart.

Chapter 1

Communicating for success

Marc Beishon, business and technology writer, outlines how business communications are set to develop apace in the early years of the new millennium

As we embark on the new millennium, we are entering an age where the use of communications – both from a business and technical standpoint – will be one of the key differentiators between successful organisations and those that get left behind.

From a business perspective, the race is on to meet the demands of consumers and business partners, who are demanding ever higher levels of service, and who are enjoying new, flexible buying channels such as the internet.

On the technical front, we are about to see a massive explosion in the availability of low-cost, high-speed telecommunications that bring together the previously separate worlds of voice and data.

The challenge for companies of all sizes is to harness this increased power to move their businesses forward, and it is the job of the telecoms operators and their huge industry of partners to deliver solutions that match business needs. However, the latter is not so straightforward, mainly because of the rapid pace of change.

Not only are there new technologies to get to grips with, the telecoms industry itself is undergoing a period of unprecedented change, with the opening up of markets previously tied to country "incumbents" and the overturning of traditional price models for basic items such as call charges and interconnection between operators.

NEW SCOPE FOR NETWORKS

The sheer scope of the "bandwidth explosion" offers a vivid taste of what's to come. Bandwidth – the capacity of networks to carry voice and data traffic – has been tightly controlled by a few main players and, therefore, relatively scarce.

There are now more than 1,000 carriers competing to provide international services, compared to fewer than 400 three years ago. "Within ten years, low cost, high capacity transmission facilities will encircle the globe - bandwidth will be a commodity, and the emphasis will move to the pricing, packaging and management of services. The successful players have still to be determined, but there will be no return to bandwidth scarcity and artificially high tariff structures," say industry analysts Ovum.

Such confidence comes from the huge growth in the internet as a catalyst for change, with some 700m people likely to be on-line worldwide by 2005. Ovum says that 83 per cent of international demand for bandwidth will come from the internet by 2005, with voice communications being the junior partner by far. What's more, it estimates that the value of business-to-consumer e-commerce transactions will be $358m by that time. This, however, will be overshadowed by the huge $2.1tn in business-to-business trading.

In the UK, several planks are now falling into place to help enable the mass take-up of the internet. A key move is the opening up to competition of the "local loop", the line that connects homes and smaller businesses to the telephone exchange. The telecoms regulator, Oftel, has recently ruled that operators other than BT will be able to upgrade these lines to fast, high-bandwidth internet channels, and has set a deadline of July 2001 for when new services can be launched to consumers and businesses.

CHARGING STRUCTURE TO CHANGE

The upgrades to lines allow a much greater amount of data to be transmitted (at least ten times more than current technology initially, and potentially much more). However, more significantly, it will facilitate the new ADSL technology – Asymetric Digital Subscriber

Line – which is set to change the way data service users are charged. ADSL allows a "permanently on" connection with an internet service provider, as it allows the protocol used on the internet to travel seamlessly to a home computer or a network in a business. Instead of dialling up and establishing a call charged on a time basis, charges will be more likely to be based on the value of information received.

BT is already upgrading 400 local exchanges to use this ADSL technology. However, ADSL is not the only way of creating high-bandwidth services. Other technologies that will all play a part are cable, digital television, satellite and the next generation of mobile phone services (see also Chapter 7 on mobiles).

In the next two years consumers and business purchasers, using the internet as a channel to get best value and service, will benefit from an increasing choice of suppliers. Conversely, the availability of a mass audience of people on the internet provides an invaluable opportunity for companies to personalise information for individuals and to target and segment a customer base.

Industry analysts expect to see a move towards a "horizontal" structure in the telecoms market, where a few "best of breed" suppliers provide a choice of building blocks for the network infrastructure and retail telecoms services, with a mass of specialist service and content providers layered on top. The internet-style method of transmission will be pervasive, and mobile connections will soon outstrip fixed lines.

COMMUNICATIONS FOR CUSTOMER SERVICE

Although data and information services will be increasingly important, the emerging picture is not one of replacement for traditional voice services. Rather, both voice and data will be carried across the same networks, and there will be increasing "synergy" between the two worlds. Nowhere is this more apparent than in the burgeoning call centre industry, which employs some 400,000 people in full or part time roles.

If the internet represents the next wave of communications, the call centre is very much the phenomenon of the present, with companies scrambling to get hold of the best 0500 and 0800 freephone numbers as they recognise the edge that free access to customer service can give.

As traditional face-to-face business takes a back seat, the call centre is also taking on automated functions that require no human intervention, such as balance checking. Companies are also implementing "web-enabled" call centres, where agents interacting with people simultaneously over the phone and through a website can, for example, guide customers to view products they want to know more about.

CUSTOMER RELATIONSHIP MARKETING

It is all part of the customer relationship marketing stakes, in which companies are seeking to understand their client base better. There is now feverish activity to integrate various back office systems, such as billing and field service applications, into the customer-facing experience.

Call centres can be as small as just a handful of agents - many companies in the SME sector are finding that a dedicated team can make all the difference to either outbound telemarketing activities, or in-bound service handling.

Meanwhile, the communications technology employed by a business can give it an overall feel of greater professionalism, or even create the impression that it is larger than it really is. Ensuring, for example, that all key staff have their own direct dial telephone numbers, perhaps coupled with an in-house cordless phone or even seamlessly integrating with a wide-area mobile handset, can end the frustration often felt by clients trying to get hold of staff.

Deploying information for both in-house and field staff is also becoming critical. The company intranet, comprising everything from sales and market book to an expense claims system has been a hot growth area in recent years. Sharing information and transactions with partners – suppliers, purchasers and consultants – is also becoming absolutely fundamental to success.

For both personal and business use another key application

area is unified messaging, which brings together voicemail, e-mail and fax in one interface. Together with a "follow-me" number, no-one need be unreachable, as they can always receive a communication sent by any method.

One development that will make life a lot easier for businesses is where telecoms operators and service providers are offering to "host" an application or service, thus removing the need for specialist in-house equipment and staff. In a world where networks are providing huge capacity, call centre and general switchboard operations can be managed remotely, as can running core applications such as a finance or e-commerce system.

Outsourcing telecoms infrastructure to handle call distribution is already standard practice, while the idea of application rental is now taking off. Rental can give a smaller company access to a top software such as the SAP enterprise resource planning (ERP) package. This allows it to enjoy the resilience and future-proofing a remote host can provide without needing to invest in either the computing platform or full licence needed to run it in-house.

In many respects, the future for communications lies in promoting the kind of "virtual" networking and interdependency that's building up in the market in any case. It may be the case that the movement to downsize, concentrate on core functions and form alliances came first. But the concerns of some telecoms operators that the vast new capacity they are building won't be used is unlikely given that any company serious about its future will need to invest in new communications technologies.

Chapter 2

The new models for business

In the e-business world there is no room for technology for technology's sake. Systems and strategic objectives must be fully aligned. This, says Rob Fisher, chief executive, Cable & Wireless Communications,may demand fundamental organisational change

The convergence of voice and data has the power to improve greatly the way we work. As companies start to use internet protocol (IP) as the basis of their local networks, it will be possible to walk up to a terminal, log on with your personal ID and know that the adjacent telephone has just become yours. No forwarding of numbers; no cancelling of previous forwards; no notes on sticky yellow labels saying "I'm now in xyz department, working with xyz". The phone becomes associated with the person who sits there at any given time, and if any calls cannot be answered they go to the right voicemail. Log on and get full access to all the information you need to do your job through a single converged set of systems.

This is no small internal revolution. It has relevance for every aspect of a business: for the accounts department and the board; for relationships with customers and suppliers. Deployed wisely, voice over IP will cut overheads, increase productivity and efficiency and, crucially, improve service. It can be seen as a strategic tool that will help win competitive advantage.

SMALL COMPANIES AND THE INTERNET
The challenge is getting this new technology accepted and in place in all companies that can profit from it. To embrace it, companies will first have to embrace the Web.

UK business has been relatively slow to do this. According to the Department of Trade and Industry, it lags behind not only America and Canada but also Scandinavia in its use of web sites. Remarkably few UK companies fully appreciate the power of the internet to create new "global" companies at low cost and to challenge older business models. At the 1999 IoD Annual Convention, the then Director General Tim Melville-Ross cited research showing that less than two per cent of companies saw the internet as any kind of threat.

Small and medium-sized enterprises (SMEs) have been the slowest to respond – to both the challenges and the opportunities. They often don't understand how the internet works, or what it can do for them. The government is actively trying to get more of them working on the Web and is even considering special rates for companies that submit tax returns electronically. The message is that the internet is not an option but a necessity.

BEST E-BUSINESS PRACTICE

Using the technology, though, is not, of itself, enough. The key is using it well. Sensible companies use the internet for:

■   *E-mail and "surfing";*

■   *As a marketing tool, putting details about products and contacts on a web page;*

■   *E-trading.*

They also know that they will inevitably one day use it for voice and data convergence.

Because they want all their staff to be confident and happy in using the internet they don't restrict its access to the chosen, senior few. They don't see it as an expensive overhead because they know it will, in the longer-term at least, cut their costs and improve their business.

Crucially, they recognise that the Web is an interactive medium. They start to make front-office systems available to customers, which starts people ordering at the click of a button.

This instantaneously sends an order electronically. After that, they progress to linking back-office systems over the internet, integrating payment and changing operational procedures to suit new types of business.

Converging data and telephony services is but a more mature phase of internet evolution, allowing call centres and front-office service centres to use the power of the internet, with the addition of point-and-click and "talk to me" facilities. Customers get improved service and facilities, and companies get more efficient operations.

Today, some businesses are actually based on internet-enabled integration of front and back office. A classic example is the bookseller Amazon.com. Everything it does revolves entirely around its web presence. Whatever it does, it thinks of the internet first, and all other channels and activities second. Now world famous, it provides an object lesson in the power of the internet.

CHANGING BUSINESS MODELS

Any company introducing or developing the use of internet technology must be aware of the knock-on effect on business processes. A supermarket is an interesting example. Being able to sit at home pointing and clicking, knowing that your groceries are going to turn up is quite seductive. It feels very good. You don't have to get into your car, traipse around a store, queue up to pay or load what you've bought. But think about the underlying business model for a moment.

When you point and click, that request has to get to somebody who can walk around the store (or around a warehouse) picking items off shelves and loading them into a trolley or onto a van. And when that is done, another person has to deliver the order. If you're not in at the time, they have to be able to deal with that. If you're unhappy with the order, they have to be able to deal with that.

The Icelands and Tescos of this world have had to recruit people specifically to pick orders, then establish a delivery infrastructure and, finally, make sure that this new process all ties in with the existing business model for selling.

E-business usually works like this. It is an exercise in creating a new business channel, usually to work alongside an existing fulfilment system. The new channel has to work well in its own right, as well as work well with what's there already.

THE FUTURE OF THE "CALL" CENTRE

There will be new models for managing customer relationships as well as for buying, selling and delivering. In a few years' time, the call centre, for example, will look, function and be managed differently. Go into one today and you will usually see wall displays showing performance statistics. You can see instantly what percentage of calls is answered in 15 or 20 seconds, how many calls are waiting in the queue and how many calls have been answered on that day. The emphasis is on calls because of the facility with which people can make them and the ease with which call statistics can be measured.

But call centres going online using new "click to talk to me" technology will not receive all requests as telephone calls. The telephone system will be converged with support systems such as the internet and the company's business systems. Customers will be asking for help via the internet and will also be e-mailing requests. Not all enquiries coming in will need to be dealt with in real time.

Operators will have to work differently and perhaps have different skills. In many instances, they will be able to see exactly what the customer sees on their screen and have a record of what the customer has been doing. This is in addition to reference information about that customer's account. These dialogues will take place in real time: the call centre operator will be helping to solve customer problems "live". It will no longer be possible to work using pre-defined scripts.

Increasingly, call centre staff will be dispersed, working from more than one physical location. This raises issues about the way they are managed. It will be essential, for example, to evaluate non real-time staff fairly alongside real-time staff and reward them accordingly.

BIG IS BAD, SMALL IS GOOD?

So technological change demands management and organisational change. As big companies build data "warehouses" to help them manage customer relationships better, this is becoming startlingly obvious. The customer-information databases on which both call centres and marketing departments depend are best built by cross-functional teams. Corporate "silos" and vertical structures discourage the spread and the sharing of information. They will become an anachronism.

Large corporates have to get all their systems, not just the network, aligned to automated working. They have to integrate their historical "legacy" and back-office systems – and the data they hold – with the new front-office office systems.

This places younger, smaller companies at an advantage. They usually do not have a juggernaut of history to pull round. For them, the "new" ways of working are often easier to implement. They may even come more "naturally", since they will have to be adopted by a smaller number of staff, often working more closely together. The internet and convergence therefore give SMEs the chance to compete not only in the same arena as the corporates but also to compete with an edge. They must not let the opportunity slip by.

Chapter 3

The e-business imperative

Why is the world going "e-crazy"? What is it about the "electronic" prefix that is driving so many new start-ups to inflated stock market values, and causing so much soul searching in traditional bricks and mortar businesses? Marc Beishon, business and technology writer, reports

It is widely recognised that electronic business models are opening up new channels for doing business, which are faster and smarter in terms of winning customers and developing relationships thereafter. But it is communications technology that underpins the brave new world of e-commerce and "e-business". Without the internet, cable TV, mobile phones and all the rest of the emerging digital communications picture, there could be no electronic business revolution.

Understanding the marriage between communications and new techniques is essential. Not only does it offer an insight into the enabling factors behind electronic business, but also provides a solid basis on which to formulate a company's in-house strategy.

GOING BEYOND E-COMMERCE

There is much more to electronic business than the activities that the term "e-commerce" implies. E-commerce has been widely used as a cover-all term for "doing business" on the internet, but most analysts now agree that it has a fairly narrow definition, related to transactions.

Setting up a basic storefront on a web site, for example, is probably the most widespread e-commerce activity. But, in reality, it may be nothing more than a shopping list of items and a standard credit card ordering mechanism. Many companies are still simply printing out an order generated on their web site and processing it manually.

Electronic business or e-business, however, encapsulates many more processes. In commercial terms, a true e-business could be electronic almost from start to finish, across the entire supply chain. While customers or other businesses place orders at a web site, all the other functions – credit card authorisation, stock check, ledger update, delivery tracking, stock reorder and so on – happen seamlessly without any human intervention. About the only manual intervention is loading the goods at a warehouse and delivering them – and in the case of a service or electronic product such as digital music, there need be no human involvement at all.

Supply chain activities are a core part of the emerging picture. Both business-to-commerce and business-to-business transactions in many industries getting the e-business treatment although, at present, it is rare to see any firm implementing more than a few functions at a time. The business-to-business market is particularly active, with companies and organisations such as government departments busily installing procurement systems, a favourite starting point in driving down the cost of supplies.

E-business is also embracing as so-called "employee self-service" applications that allow staff to carry out a range of processes for themselves. These could include filing expense claims, booking holidays, registering sick leave – all internal functions that can be managed over a company "intranet" network available only to authorised users.

Even the most widely used tool of the internet- electronic mail - is a valuable mechanism for doing business. Many professionals now prefer to receive e-mails rather than paper-based communications, and a well-structured e-mail, say comprising company news and latest product details, can take the place of a traditional mail shot.

E-mail can also, naturally, be considerably cheaper than direct postal mail or fax, but like all communications, needs to be used sparingly in accordance with a recipient's wishes.

COMBINING CALL CENTRES WITH THE WEB

But, e-business goes much further than just taking an order in the customer-facing environment. The call centre has become the avenue for dealing with people on the phone, segmenting calls into easily managed enquiries and instructions, with the more advanced having sophisticated computer-telephony (CTI).

The call centre of the future, however, is likely to be linked to a web site. A customer may be offered the choice of clicking a "button" which requests an agent to call them. Then, a simultaneous call and web session can take place, with an agent guiding the customer through images and descriptions of products, perhaps even sending special packages of information to the caller's computer.

One of the fiercest contests today is between companies trying to gain competitive advantage through providing the most effective, and pleasurable, buying experiences for customers. The debate about customer relationship management (CRM), and how companies align themselves to be more customer facing, is moving on to so-called ERM, or electronic relationship management.

The aim of ERM is to present the customer with just one organisation, rather than a set of departments through which they have to navigate. This is achieved by integrating all the channels that a customer may want to choose into one grand interface.

US IS LEADING THE WAY

ERM is now a sort of e-business holy grail for UK companies. Meanwhile in the US, which leads the way in so many business trends, large companies are taking these kind of steps, often for pragmatic reasons.

Take the example of one mobile phone company which has allowed customers to check remaining credit balances online, freeing up call centre staff for more complex enquiries, and also providing an "added value" service that could help to cut defections in an industry notorious for high customer churn.

It may sound simple but the integration steps needed to give potentially many thousands of customers a window onto their accounts makes this type of system a complex engineering exercise. This personalisation feature will also become a significant differentiator in business-to-business markets. Just as consumers may want to log on to check their balance and credit history, life can be made easier for business purchasers, who can be presented with both a selection of items and news relevant to their needs as well as a note of what they bought last time.

In the e-business market companies need partners like never before. Despite the global reach that a company web site can give, there is much to be gained by participating in the many specialist "portals" that are springing up. Business portal sites are often designed to bring buyers and sellers together, and offer vital marketing clout for smaller firms in the supply chain. Enterprise software suppliers are among the firms busily setting up industry specific portals.

THE UBIQUITOUS INTERNET

The common denominator for all these merging e-business applications is the internet, which provides the huge advantage of a single accessible network for mixed traffic – data, video, pictures, documents and even voice. Even the smallest company may benefit from looking at a simple network that allows staff to browse online, send and receive e-mail and also integrates this process with voice calls, so that they have a direct dial-in phone number, and can access a client phone directory from their PCs.

Technology selection for e-business is crucial, especially as the internet world is still in its infancy, with lots of work still to be done on issues such as security, business-to-business transaction processing standards and sheer robustness and scalability. However, for companies with limited information technology expertise, the way forward in e-business can look far from straightforward. There is now a huge number of suppliers purporting to offer everything from web-enabled switchboards, to security tools for business "extranets", to hosted solutions for almost every aspect of e-business.

Then there are trends at the sharp end. For example, analysts are expecting a boom in so-called "m-commerce" (mobile commerce), with the new generation of faster mobile phone technology enabling people to conduct more of their businesses on the move.

The internet is also likely to make an impact on the retail shop floor, with interactive kiosks that customers can use to browse catalogues, and new types of point-of-sale terminals that face the customer and offer such attractions as instant loyalty schemes.

All these solutions require communications building blocks, in terms of networks and software tools. In fact, almost any type of communications technology can be seen as part of the e-business scenario, when its use can be related to a business process. E-business is about empowerment, from installing relatively simple personal tools that save time and give customers greater access, to securing a transparent integration of all channels.

For most companies, it has never been more important to seek advice about marrying business goals with the appropriate technology. Act now, before it's too late.

Chapter 4

The workplace of the 21st century

Information and communications technologies will eventually mean the end of nine-to-five, office-bound working. This, says Wes McGregor, director of Advanced Workplace Associates, has far-reaching implications for the management of both people and property

The world of work is changing more radically and more quickly than ever before. Intense global competition and rapid developments in information and communications technologies (ICT) are challenging past assumptions of stability in the workplace.

However, the design of many workplaces reflects old approaches to work and therefore fails to take into account either the current or the future needs of people and businesses. It will have to change. The "new design" must be predicated on a real understanding of the needs of people, work processes and businesses, in the knowledge that what are presently regarded as innovative and challenging work practices and relationships will be commonplace in 15 years' time.

RESPONDING TO CHANGING NEEDS

Today, standing still is not an option. Those slow to adapt will be overtaken by events. Organisations need to be more responsive to changing market conditions and more innovative in addressing them – otherwise, they will not win competitive advantage.

Traditional organisations and workplace environments buckle under the strain of these new demands. They were never designed to cope with rapid market changes because they have as their roots the outmoded concepts of hierarchy and permanence.

THE E-BUSINESS

Increasingly, much of the normal discourse of business is being conducted electronically. E-commerce offers more than a means to change sales and delivery channels to a much lower cost base and to enter markets that previously have been the preserve of others. It also offers a way to re-engineer across organisational boundaries.

E-commerce renders obsolete many traditional – and costly – channels to market such as branch networks. Many markets will see new entrants who will use ICT to be selective in the areas of business they develop, cherry-picking those that are either high margin or have the greatest growth potential, or both. Not for them the historic real estate baggage of their long serving competitors; they have replaced bricks with "clicks", posing a serious threat to traditional organisations.

FLEXIBLE WORKING

The term flexible working is used to describe "alternative" work patterns to the older models. In the most radical examples, people work where and when they want to – provided, of course, they continue to meet the company's needs.

Flexible working may embrace the idea of hot desking, where people share an office workplace for some of the time they are in the building. It may also embrace "hotelling", where the workplace is readied for the arrival of a worker who has booked the space in advance. For an increasing number of people, however, it means working from home or "teleworking" from remote centres that are electronically "connected" to the central "hub".

Information and communications technologies make an expansive geography available, enabling people to work from the premises of customers and suppliers, satellite buildings, telecentres and business centres, transit locations and, of course, their own home. The principal objective is to match the requirements of the tasks to be performed to the most effective time-space relationship that can be achieved.

"EMPOWERING" THE INDIVIDUAL

For many people, the attraction of working from home is the ability to achieve a better balance between their working and their personal lives. The key component appears to be choice. If an individual is given the ability to choose where and when they work, they are likely to experience much reduced levels of stress.

"Telecommuters" can choose to work before commuter trains start running or long after businesses' "workspace" is closed. They can "commute" by telephone and e-mail instead of public transport, can move house without moving job and don't have to ask anyone's permission to take "time off" to see the school play, celebrate a special event or enjoy a spell of good weather.

Of course, flexible working patterns must be appropriate for the tasks to be performed – otherwise, they will not achieve the objective of reducing overheads and increasing efficiency. Danger lurks around the corner where the introduction of new flexible styles of working has more to do with the business's failure to forecast its accommodation needs than its drive to improve productivity or the quality of life for its workers.

To be effective, a workplace must be the successful integration of the physical environment, the information environment and the customer-service environment, set in a context of protocols guiding their use. Seen in this way, the workplace is a tool that should support business processes, enabling people to work anytime, any place and anywhere.

BUSINESS LOCATION

ICT has profound implications for both the locus of work and for urban property markets. The building boom of the mid-1980s created many very large-scale office developments, mostly in city centre locations. As workers become "globally mobile" without leaving their own homes, these will rapidly become white elephants.

The location of many businesses is becoming much less critical to their effective servicing of the needs of customers. ICT advances are allowing organisations to compete by virtualising the nature of their businesses: work activities are becoming location-independent. An organisation increasingly exists by virtue of its technology, not by virtue of its property.

A continuously improving IT infrastructure is one of the imperatives for sustaining increases in business productivity and profitability. Consequently, issues relating to the possible application of technology to almost all aspects of business operations, and hence the mode and place of work, will need to feature prominently in the strategic plans of every organisation. Accommodation strategies will be shaped by the way organisations employ ICT, as much as they will be determined by the numbers of people required by the business.

Technology gives the opportunity to send raw data to workers located in other global time zones. Information can be processed while the UK sleeps and made available for the start of the next day's trading. The formation of international skills pools and the development of offshore support centres not only extend the working cycle but enable businesses to tap labour markets that operate with a much lower cost base than the UK.

ORGANISATIONAL STRUCTURES

The effective business does not try to do everything itself. Instead, it establishes a network of relationships with other organisations – in some cases even competing businesses – so that it can readily and speedily access specialist knowledge. A web of best-practice operations, wherever they may be located, allows the creation of high-quality, low-cost, new products and services for customers on demand. Strategic alliances, joint ventures, partnering and sub-contracting – all of these are born out of businesses' desire to focus on "what we do best", while putting the rest in expert hands.

Virtual businesses will no longer produce goods or services themselves but orchestrate the actions of others, many of whom will never actually see the end-product.

ICT has the power both to flatten and extend organisations, beyond traditional boundaries. Flexible working will hasten the demise of archaic functional silos, replacing them with process-focused, cross-functional work groups.

"WRONG" AND "RIGHT" WORKING

The provision of workspace should be a direct response to the needs of people and support them in their work endeavours. Yet most organisations remain wedded to an old organisational model where:

- *Property is the major fixed cost;*

- *Property agreements are based on timescales measured in decades rather than hours;*

- *Workspace is slow and costly to adapt; and*

- *Workplaces are inappropriate for emerging work practices.*

Increasingly, the emphasis in human resources is on empowering the individual, on providing the tools so that he or she can carry out his or her job in the most satisfying as well as the most satisfactory way. The workplace needs to be capable of meeting the functional needs of the individual and his/her work processes as never before. The "traditional" approach of providing one dedicated workplace for every employee is failing to address true operational needs. This is because the majority of people today carry out a wide range of activities. Styles of working that were largely based on mono-tasking – carrying out a single, repetitive activity –are dying.

Right working is an approach based on providing each individual with a range of taskplaces at which they can work according to their varying needs throughout the working day. Quietness, group interaction, confidentiality, telephone communications – these are needs that the various taskplace settings must meet. The appropriate technology must be deployed to enable telephone calls, e-mail and data transactions to be made from any location, and fully supported all day, every day.

CONCLUSION

As businesses progressively come to terms with the fact that the quality of work environment they provide for their people directly affects the quality of their work, then flexible working practices will become the norm.

It is important to recognise, however, that there is no single, universal solution. Instead, there is likely to be a range of solutions that will be required to enable the organisation to "flex" to suit the changing business circumstances.

Although flexible working is principally geared to improving the performance of people, and should only be adopted as a result of extensive investigation into its suitability, it can also make major contributions to improving the way workspace is used.

The future of work will be much more about delivering to a specification than about "putting in" a pre-determined quantity of hours in a specific location. Managers will have to learn new skills to address the needs of flexible and virtual organisations, which comprise a network of people using communications technologies to work from many locations and for many businesses.

ICT is the enabler and the liberator that makes possible innovative ways to work. But it must always be kept in mind that the pace at which an organisation can make the necessary changes will be dependent on the speed at which its people – not its technology – develops.

Investing to deliver business Internet and IP services.

Business Made Simpler

CABLE & WIRELESS

Chapter 5

Communications for customer service

Companies can annoy and even lose customers through poorly targeted "junk" mail, irritating faxes or robotic answering services. Stephen Morrell, consultant at market analysts Datamonitor, warns that a company is only as strong as its weakest channel

Before the mid-1980s, the single predominant channel for the delivery of customer service was face to face interaction between the vendor and the consumer. Then, over a very short period of time new channels sprang up.

Not everything is as new as it seems of course. Sales by catalogue started in the late 1800s. Their successor, the household mailshot, took on more accuracy as people's postcodes and data about their shopping habits began to be used by "direct mailing" houses to reach named individuals. These electronic databases also made it easier to use the telephone, and the fax to reach potential customers. These produced a whole new learning process for companies to work out how best to manage them to deliver customer service. Direct mail was often insufficiently targeted, call centres (modest by today's warehouse size operations) were used for massive, cold-calling sales campaigns, and "junk" faxes became an irritant for businesses.

CUT THE COST AND LOSE THE CUSTOMER

In the early and mid-1990s, customer service technology for many companies was still primarily about cutting costs internally, rather than improving the quality of service. Technologies such as interactive voice response (IVR), the dreaded automatic answering system which greets many telephone customers), predictive diallers (which call as many numbers as possible for outbound marketing campaigns) and even the bedrock of the call centre, the ACD (automated call distributor), were about cutting down time to answer, and therefore staff costs. The goal was simple: have fewer agents answer or place more calls more quickly. The modern call centre thus sprung into existence as part of a broad cost-cutting trend, not because companies wanted to give better customer service.

However, customer enthusiasm for certain types of telebusiness, such as direct insurance and telebanking, gave call centres a real boost, providing levels of service which could not be rivalled in traditional branches. Much of this increased efficiency was down to the need to implement new forms of technology, as every agent needed to have the same access to customer and product infor-mation, regardless of geography: simply put, employees could no longer keep customer records on paper files.

At the same time as this move towards increased efficiency and access to customer information went into full swing, the cost-cutting thrust of customer service managers was tempered by the increasing need to generate revenues from the call centre. Forward looking enterprises began to view their customer service operations as profit centres, not cost centres.

THE CUSTOMER SHOULD DECIDE

This new appreciation has had a profound effect. However, it is a myth that a company, which depends on providing a high standard of customer service as part of its entire offering, can be the sole decider as to which channels this service will be delivered through. Customers, whether consumers or other businesses, are demanding the ability to contact an enterprise by telephone and fax, and now via e-mail and the Web.

The critical question that firms must ask themselves is "Do these channels give the same level of service to customers?" Some companies tend to think that simply opening new channels for customers is enough to satisfy their customer base and give them an advantage over the competition. However, a company which goes only so far down the multimedia route will itself suffer: a business is only as strong as its weakest channel. If a company offers a new channel for customer service, its customers will expect it to be at least as effective as existing services.

TWO SIDES OF THE SAME COIN

It is only relatively recently, in the late 1990s, that the majority of firms began to realise that customer service and customer acquisition were two sides of the same coin: ignoring the former, in favour of the absolutist pursuit of the latter, is simply an unsustainable strategy in a highly competitive marketplace. And so, armed with ever more sophisticated communication and information management technologies, companies are responding to these new competitive pressures in two critical ways.

First, they are focusing on connecting their call centres and customer service agents to customers over new media, such as the web and e-mail, while still maintaining high levels of voice-based service. Second, companies are focusing on the automation of front office processes and their integration with both customer services functions and back office functions. These two trends roughly define what has come to be known as Customer Relationship Management (CRM).

Sales force automation has been closely followed by the automation of marketing and service functions. New CRM software allows for the capture, tracking and analysis of prospect, customer and enterprise-level information across all front office business processes. The best CRM software also links to back office databases and enterprise resource planning (ERP) applications, allowing for powerful links between customer demand and back office accounting and manufacturing processes.

Customer and company information is now, and will increasingly be, available to all employees who have contact with customers; as a result customers will increasingly find themselves in a "dialogue" with the enterprise, rather than engaging in a series of one-off encounters. Marketing, sales and service will no longer be divorced from each other, but will instead be seen as continuous stages in the development of a "customer relationship".

TIME TO RING IN THE CHANGES

In view of these trends, Datamonitor research suggests that call centres are on the verge of a transformation. At present they are overwhelmingly voice-based, but within the next five years there will be a huge growth in the number of contact centres fully connected to the internet, able to route and queue inbound messages to appropriately skilled, "blended" agents who will be able to respond to web queries, e-mails and voice calls in quick succession.

The internet provides a unique opportunity for companies to deliver high quality, sophisticated customer service at reduced costs. This is primarily due to three new technologies: automated e-mail response software, Web self-service software and software which enables web-based live-agent help.

Automated e-mail response software analyses the content of incoming e-mails, formulates a response, and automatically generates an outgoing message, referring difficult or problematic cases to agents for the purpose of checking response accuracy. Web self-service software enables customers to make queries at the company's web site, and uses case-based reasoning to access knowledge bases in order to generate a response. This prevents the need for the customer to compose a formal e-mail or to call into a call centre to resolve the issue at hand. Finally, Web-based, live agent, help software enables customer service agents to "push" specific Web pages to a customer's PC as he or she browses the corporate web site, and to initiate chat sessions about specific needs or products on offer.

So while customers will have a host of new methods to contact the company, it will have increasing customer information at its disposal. Agents at these new internet-enabled contact centres will have access to the history of a customer or prospect's interaction with the organisation, whether that be with the marketing, sales or customer service department, presenting agents with the ability to turn service interactions into opportunities to cross-sell and up-sell.

This "integrated channel management" will allow for a personalisation of sales and service which was, until now, simply not possible in a call centre or internet environment. The effect of these new technologies on agents will be substantial: combined with the advent of reliable speech recognition technologies, the ability for customers to resolve simple queries over the web or e-mail will free agents to work on more complex enquiries. The automation of low level customer service and concomitant agent "upskilling" will entail previously phone bound customer service representatives being called on to manage communications over the web, compose written e-mail responses to complex questions, and increase their product awareness in order to identify new selling opportunities.

CUSTOMER CENTRIC QUALITY AND COMPLEXITY

The overall implications for business of the new trends in customer service delivery are clear. Companies must ensure that customers can contact their service representatives via all media, including the Web and e-mail.

Service delivered over the internet should be of as high a quality as that delivered over the telephone. More than ever, agents will be called on to perform complex customer services and sales tasks as lower value-added services are automated. So, while a recent Datamonitor survey of call centre managers revealed that Web enablement decreased cost levels in 53 per cent of cases and increased service levels in 67 per cent of cases, it is crucial for companies to view this business trend not as cost centric, but as customer centric. These new technologies offer businesses the opportunity to both improve customer services, and quite literally, make them pay.

Explore your full e-business potential.

Business Made Simpler

CABLE & WIRELESS

Chapter 6

Voice and data integration

In as little as five years, the use of internet technology to carry voice traffic could be the norm. No company, says Stuart Keeping, product director, IP Applications, Cable & Wireless Communications, can now afford to ignore the business benefits

Voice and data communications can now be delivered over a single network. Until recently, the cost savings and business benefits of such integration have been enjoyed chiefly by big enterprises that have their own private networks and dedicated call centres. However, as the technology matures and becomes a commodity, it begins also to make sense for small and medium-sized enterprises. Even if they think it does not look like a good investment for them now, it almost certainly soon will.

Voice/data integration can offer companies immediate operational savings both through lower direct communication costs, and by having just one network to manage. Even for a company without its own voice and/or data network, administering voice and data communications as separate processes increases overheads.

Of greater long-term significance than the financial benefits, however, is the use of the technology to help manage relationships with customers across a variety of channels. Today's call centres can log and update customer information on a centralised database, providing a comprehensive record of the customer's behaviour and buying habits. Integration will enable call centres of the future to collate information from not merely telephone callers but also customers using the Web, interactive television and mobile phones.

Customers are in a position to select their preferred medium and, in many cases, this may change as the relationship with the vendor develops. Initial contact may stem from a speculative e-mail enquiry and switch to a telephone helpline to secure additional information or support. Computer telephony integration (CTI) will enable vendors to maintain continuity and consistent levels of service across all these channels.

CTI also enhances a company's workflow processes, enabling the conversion of information from one format into another for ease of storage, analysis and manipulation. Voice calls can be "recorded" and logged, e-mail and postal correspondence can be similarly scanned and stored on the same database, and displayed in a variety of reports and alerts.

Although few SMEs run full-blown dedicated call centres, many do take orders, enquiries and customer service calls over the telephone and so could benefit from the same sort of voice/data integration facilities. The ability to route incoming calls intelligently to the right person and tap into relevant computer based information about that person could yield significant cost savings and service benefits.

CONTRACTING OUT

Some SMEs use a third party to provide call centre services. In this way, they obtain all the features of a big call centre without having to make the investment in the equipment and the software themselves.

In the future, they will also increasingly turn to third parties to manage the customer information databases on which call-centres depend. There is a fast growing trend towards application service provision (ASP), whereby core business applications such as order processing and customer service management are run offsite by a third party – perhaps, the third party that also provides the call centre services.

For many SMEs, ASPs provide a way to gain access to larger-scale, more resilient computing facilities and to avoid the need for expensive in-house IT expertise. They should not, of course, be hired without paying due regard both to the IT strategy of the business and its longer term needs, and to the developments that are shaping voice/data integration technology. This chapter gives some of the technological background against which decisions should be made.

DATA TRAFFIC

The first thing you need to know is that it is now voice that is being integrated into data networks rather than the other way round. This is simply because the volume of traffic in data networks is growing rapidly while voice traffic is almost static.

Data traffic is already determining how global networks grow and, within 10 years, will exceed voice by a factor of about 50 to one. (Systems that protect voice transmission at the expense of data may not, therefore be viable in the long term – see Linde Gas case study, chapter 10.)

The growing insignificance of voice in volume terms means that it will go on becoming cheaper. Furthermore, the method of charging for telecommunications services will change from the current models based on time and, in the case of some data services, on transmission rate, to ones based on content. In future, you could, for example, be charged per e-mail transmitted.

VARIATIONS IN VOICE QUALITY

The second point is that all networks will be based on the internet protocol (IP) and that this raises important performance issues. Having been optimised for data, IP networks currently offer lower-quality voice transmission. As the internet is developed and new versions of IP are implemented on it as well as within private networks, this will change; at the moment, though, it remains a consideration.

The gravity of the performance problem depends on what type of IP network voice is being transmitted over. There are three kinds of IP network: the internet, a private IP network within a company, and a public IP network.

Over the internet, no level of service can be guaranteed for voice or data: other users can swamp particular parts of the network at any time, and there is no way of knowing exactly what path a particular packet of data will take.

For now, the internet cannot be relied on for most business voice transmissions, and certainly not for conversations with customers. (It may, however, be acceptable for some internal conversations, particularly over international routes, where calls will be charged at local rates.)

PRIVATE IP NETWORKS

In the case of private IP networks, set up originally for internal data traffic only, quality depends entirely on how the system is implemented. If sufficient network capacity is provided, and the right equipment installed, voice transmitted over the network should match GSM cellular quality and even compete with that carried over the public network.

However, two points need to be made. First, IP networks behave differently as far as voice is concerned from traditional telephone networks. Whereas the latter have a fixed capacity so that a particular link is either available or engaged, IP networks have no specific cut off point. This means that as loading increases beyond a given point, quality deteriorates – even though calls can still be made. (It is possible, though, to configure an IP network in such a way that further calls are barred once a certain number of simultaneous calls are in progress. This ensures that a specified level of quality is maintained.)

MIXING NEW AND OLD

The second point is that the right equipment needs to be installed to integrate voice with an existing IP data network. The good news here is that it is not necessary to install a new network to carry voice over IP. A typical organisation will have phones attached to a private branch exchange (PBX) and PCs connected via a local area network (LAN) through routing devices to an IP network.

The migration to an all-IP network can begin by connecting the PBX to the IP routing devices via a gateway that handles the necessary signalling and protocol conversion. But it is important that the gateway is of the right type and capacity; the smaller company will have to refer to a consultancy or systems integrator for advice. The end game is to do away with the PBX altogether, and have all voice functions provided by the IP network. (It is already possible to build an IP network capable of providing all the essential functions of a PBX without needing a gateway. The latest IP routing devices from major networking system vendors such as Cisco now incorporate voice support.)

VIRTUAL PRIVATE NETWORKS

The third type of IP network, from an internet services provider or public telephone carrier, may well provide some guarantee over the timing of data delivery and therefore be suitable for business-quality voice transmission. Such networks usually deliver data or voice traffic between pre-determined points and are often referred to as virtual private networks (VPNs). This is because they simulate the operation of a private network interconnecting different sites within a given organisation.

It is possible to extend the VPN concept to other companies or individuals that subscribe to the same service provider – or to the same "group" of service providers. Telecommunications companies and internet services providers will join forces through bilateral and multilateral agreements to make VPN services available across a greater geographical spread and to a greater number of customers. Thus, high-quality voice transmission over internet protocol will eventually become standard.

CUSTOMER-SERVICE APPLICATIONS

The cost benefits of voice over IP are significant for both service provider and subscriber but it is its power to offer better customer service that is really exciting interest.

In what are increasingly crowded marketplaces, quality of service is seen as the key differentiator between companies and the only guaranteed way to retain customers. As mentioned earlier, some of the most obvious customer-service applications for voice/

data integration are in call centres. Computer telephony integration (CTI) within call centres has been possible for some years without voice over IP. CTI can be delivered with separate voice and data networks, providing the two are linked in the right way. But voice over IP brings new possibilities in Web-enabled centres.

A potential customer, for example, may browse an e-commerce site and then want to call somebody either for more information, or to complete the purchase, perhaps not wanting to trust the internet with a credit card number. With voice over IP, it is possible to establish a voice connection almost instantaneously within the internet session – particularly useful for users who only have one telephone line. (Some network equipment vendors such as Nortel already support this function.)

PRINCIPAL APPLICATIONS FOR VOICE OVER IP

■ Toll bypass – using the internet or private IP network to bypass the long distance telephone network and make calls at local rates;

■ Fax;

■ Voice messaging;

■ E-commerce, where conversations can be held within an internet session;

■ Unified messaging, bringing voice messaging, fax, and e-mail together;

■ Use of PC for phone calls and internet access.

UNIFIED MESSAGING

Unified messaging, another application for voice over IP, also improves channels of communication – both between companies and their customers and between internal departments. It enables users to have a single mailbox for voice, fax and e-mail.

Your e-mail address then becomes both your phone and fax number, and all messages can be accessed from the same box. A mobile phone, for example, will use either a small display or voice synthesis to play back e-mail and fax messages. (Note that for both fax and voice messaging, the quality of the IP network is not an issue: because live conversation is not involved, the transmission can take as long as is necessary for all the information to get through.)

Many other applications will emerge once voice over IP becomes widely deployed. Telephony carriers such as Cable & Wireless Communications predict that the majority of their voice traffic will be running over IP within five years. So the phenomenon cannot be ignored much longer, even by small companies.

Chapter 7

The third mobile revolution

Mobile phones, offering cheaper and higher speed access to services such as the internet for both business users and consumers are just round the corner. Frank Williams, business and technology, writer explains how the wireless future is coming ever closer

As we start the new decade the massive growth of mobile users seen in the 1990s continues to surge and a host of new, wireless-based applications are emerging. With digital GSM, the second generation (2G) of mobile technology, well established, the third generation (3G) of high-speed, internet communications to all manner of portable devices now lies before us.

An estimated 24m people in the UK were estimated to have mobiles as the new millennium began, 10m more than last New Year. Pre-paid call charge packages in the UK have accounted for a major part of this increase in mobile users. Analysts estimate that nearly 37m people will be using mobiles by 2003. Worldwide, it is estimated there will be 535m mobile users by 2003, 10 per cent of e-commerce will be through mobiles – "m-commerce" – and more than 600m internet-enabled phones will be in operation between 2002 and 2005.

MOBILES WITH EVERYTHING

This large customer base will be the target of a whole range of new services. Digital data services are well known to the business community. The logjam for the public is how to increase the speed and lower the cost at which data can be handled by mobiles. To fulfill this need, the telecommunications industry has developed a range of new mobile technology and applications offering mobile internet browsers and personal digital assistants (PDAs) which are intended to transmit and receive video film. Soon we will wonder how we coped with today's slow speeds and limited mobile data traffic such as faxes, sending and retrieving short e-mails, basic web page access and short messaging services (SMS).

SMS's low-cost way of sending and receiving text messages on mobiles is now a popular "enabler" for field force applications and only needs a PC and a clutch of mobile handsets to get started. The popularity of SMS also owes much to its reliability. It works as a "store and forward" mechanism, effectively guaranteeing the delivery of messages, which can also be accessed when someone switches on a mobile after being out of range. It can also be combined with other technologies to create a complete mobile solution in markets such as transportation and distribution.

The size of most mobile phone screens has been a limiting factor, but products such as Nokia's well-established Communicator, combining phone and PDA, have helped overcome viewing difficulties. Other PDAs, such as the Psion range or 3Com's latest Palm Pilots, can link cordlessly to a mobile phone via an infrared port, so they become portable message centres.

TRACKING TECHNOLOGIES

The majority of us are familiar with the global positioning system (GPS) receiver, which helps pinpoint geographical location by satellite. This technology can also be used to feed back route details to HQ via SMS and enable a vehicle driver to open a voice channel. In-cab terminals can handle all this, plus the printing out vital proof of delivery notes to be signed (and the faxing of a signature so that an invoice can be raised).

Other uses include automatically monitoring the temperature of refrigerated trucks and triggering alarm messages. Small firms need no longer be limited by the cost of specialist radio networks but can use public mobile networks.

Another application attracting a lot of interest is mobile location of individuals, not just tracking a vehicle or consignment.

The mobile network can work out a "fix" on someone's location using adapted handsets. A user looking for a hotel room, for example, could send an SMS message with their location, to a control centre, which can then send back details of the nearest company approved hotel. Other applications, such as the Traffic-master and AA Personal Roadwatch traffic information services, are already in extensive use.

MORE FOR LESS

Many new applications on existing mobile phones have been restricted by the lack of sufficient "bandwidth" capacity, needed to carry large amounts of data. Full internet pages, for example, with colour and pictures, have a very large data content and it has been costly and slow to receive them by mobile phone.

The next thrust is remote access for large amounts of data for the general public. Also, with increasing numbers of professionals working away from base (and many now don't have any fixed desk), there is an urgent need for reliable communications for accessing the same levels of information enjoyed by office-based colleagues.

Being able to access the latest sales figures, marketing "book", e-mails, spreadsheets and other databases while on the move makes flexible working so much easier and allows salespeople to make a complex enquiry about the configuration of an order while the customer looks on.

New software is improving the service, for example, to ensure automatic resumption of data traffic over mobile when a connection is broken. Mobiles can also be part of the corporate phone system so you can be reached through a single phone number wherever you are.

Poor coverage is the bane of mobile users. So, networks are expanding base stations for weak areas and boosting capacity to cope with overload in dense user areas. Micro-base stations can be found inside buildings to guarantee indoor reception. The latest major project is a London Underground system to allow passengers to use their mobiles.

LITTLE PACKETS

The year 2000 will see the roll-out of new services that will radically change the picture of mobile data and information services. They will mirror, but also have to compete and liaise with, the changes which have taken place on cable. These are already coming on stream through the "copper pair" wires (the fixed phone lines) for the home and business, namely the delivery of internet-style communications and video on demand.

In the mobile context, the essential difference is that data is sent in "packets" only when required, allowing a connection to be available but not permanently enabled.

An enhancement to some GSM networks, that will spread in 2000, is General Packet Radio Service (GPRS). This will give users, armed with a new generation of terminals, a much faster route to mobile data services, and will also allow a differential charging regime. A professional could log on to an office network in the morning on his or her mobile, and then automatically receive data and e-mails throughout the day, charged by the amount of data sent, not the time connected (as at present). For example, an estate agent viewing a new property could use GPRS to send pictures straight from his digital camera to a potential buyer.

TAILOR-MADE SMARTPHONES

Another major growth area is Wireless Application Protocol (WAP). This emerging standard, tailors information on the internet for access on mobile devices, and is already available for existing GSM networks using new "smartphone" handsets with larger screens. This can already handle applications such as improved on-line banking or travel information.

WAP will come into its own with the faster speeds offered by GPRS, which itself is an interim step on the way to the "third generation" (3G) of mobile technology (GPRS has been dubbed "2.5G"). 3G will offer even faster speeds, and major players are already bidding for licenses in a number of countries. This technology will be a hugely expensive undertaking for operators, but one that will almost certainly repay their investment. For example, the technologies used in both GPRS and 3G offer a much more efficient way of using "radio space" than existing systems.

As people get used to services such as unified messaging, (where all voicemail, e-mails and faxes can be accessed in one "mailbox"), on-line banking, electronic cash and internet shopping, they will want to do all this wherever they are. But when will it happen? The first 3G networks will be running by 2002, but mass take-up in markets such as the UK isn't expected until 2005.

The door to the mass market for high-speed home internet and digital TV is just opening. New mobile services will have to be keenly priced to compete and many users will need to be persuaded to bear the cost of upgrading to more powerful handsets and PDAs. The picture will not be made clearer by the plethora of new portable terminals which will be competing to win market share on price and technical capacity.

The challenge for the telecoms industry is to help people "interwork" seamlessly between fixed and mobile technologies. As you walk through your front door, your portable communicator may switch to the communication base of your TV set-top box or the terminal in your kitchen fridge door. The mobile phone which also receives TV channels is already on sale – the mobile videophone is just a mini-camera away.

Chapter 8

The practical applications of convergence

The internet has become the channel for a range of services which customers used to perform for themselves, leaving them to concentrate on their core businesses. Nick Langley, business and technology writer, outlines the various technologies

The convergence of voice and data is opening up a wealth of new possibilities in IT and telephony services. It has given a boost to IT and telephony outsourcing providers. Use of the internet means costs of delivery of services are coming down. Communications technologies like audio and videoconferencing have a new wealth of functionality.

Meanwhile, the management of these services is increasingly being handled by specialist carriers, freeing up companies' in-house resources to capitalise on the customer information from the range of channels at their disposal. These new levels of customer and management information are by no means restricted to the blue-chip sector, with the SME market increasingly outsourcing the management of telephone and internet-based channels to market, to focus instead on their core business.

APPLICATION SERVICE PROVIDERS

There will come a time – and it may not be far off – when few companies will own and manage computer servers. Instead, they will have access, via the internet, to applications running at data centres owned by a new kind of outsourcing company: ASPs, or application service providers.

ASPs provide larger organisations with an alternative to installing and maintaining applications internally, and give smaller companies access to "best of breed" applications they wouldn't otherwise be able to afford. Apart from substantial savings in software investment, the advantages include no longer having to depend on scarce and expensive software specialists, and enabling the IT function to concentrate on core business objectives rather than technology issues.

ASPs are already established as suppliers of enterprise resource planning applications, which are notoriously expensive and time-consuming to implement. Even at the other end of the scale, moves are afoot to rent rather than buy software, including Microsoft Office applications. The attraction of the rental market is that users will have constant access to the latest application upgrades, and can adopt a pay-as-you-use approach to minimise their outlays. Alternatively, the service may be provided at a fixed monthly cost.

Application hosting can also be provided by internet service providers (ISPs) and telcos. Such organisations will take on a company's e-business applications, handling every stage from designing the systems to setting up arrangements with logistics companies, invoicing customers and banking your earnings.

There's a point where ASP and application hosting services merge into more traditional outsourcing. Some ASPs will manage your entire IT infrastructure, including networking and the desktop.

INTERNET TELEPHONY SERVICE PROVIDERS

Some internet service providers are evolving into ITSPs (internet telephony service providers). The telcos are countering the threat from start-up internet telephony providers by offering their own services, and there are "clearing houses", set up by the likes of AT&T and Telia, who will handle all the agreements and billing arrangements with other carriers and countries with a single contract.

Ian Stevenson, a principal analyst at research and consultancy company Ovum, warns that carriers that want to compete in the internet telephony business must invest in technology that bridges the gap between voice, data and internet platforms. "Incumbent carriers, particularly in Europe, must break away from their conservative attitude towards new voice services, or lose the opportunity to new entrants.

"A key first step is to provide a link from the PSTN (public switched telephone network) service platforms to IP (internet protocol). This allows traditional telephony to be delivered to any IP access point that supports the required class of service. While this provides a means for new entrant carriers to compete in IP telephony, it also opens the door to new applications that combine the best of the Web's worldwide marketing capabilities with the comfort and security of a person-to-person call."

Customers too must embrace the new technologies in order to remain competitive. However, according to a 1999 survey by the catalogue network product vendor Black Box, the message has yet to get through. Ninety-five per cent of companies interviewed had no voice and data integration, and 31 per cent hadn't a clue what the term meant. Eight per cent believed they would never have a need to integrate voice and data.

"Voice and data integration is commonly perceived as all hype and no substance," according to Black Box's technical director Patrick Hudgell. "While bemoaning the lack of available bandwidth, many companies fail to appreciate that voice and data integration is one way out of their problems."

UNIFIED MESSAGING

Most of us use at least three different messaging technologies in our everyday work: telephone, e-mail and fax. The volumes of messages received using these technologies is on the increase, and dealing with messages takes up a growing part of the working day. Unified messaging offers a way of putting all these messages into a single "in-box", where they can be dealt with in priority order. The same interface that lists e-mails could also list faxes and voicemails, with details of who contacted us, and when.

Unified messaging also provides a way of keeping in touch with messages when travelling. Put a call through to pick up your voicemails, and a speech synthesiser can also tell you what e-mails and faxes you've received, giving you the option to have them read to you. This needs no specialist equipment – any domestic, office, hotel or mobile phone can be used. You can also arrange to have faxes redirected to a convenient number, or e-mails and even voicemails sent to a multimedia PC, using voice over IP. You can delete the junk faxes and e-mails.

Companies can either install their own unified messaging systems, or buy a service from a fixed or mobile telephone company. Mobile operators are already beginning to offer notification of faxes over the phone. Internet Service Providers (ISPs) are likely to offer these services as they attempt to break into the voice telephony market. Pricing strategies will vary widely depending on whether the supplier makes most of its revenue from internet services or voice, but 10-15 per person per month is typical.

If a company decides to install its own, it will be dealing with suppliers like Lucent, Active Voice, Applied Voice Technologies and Callware. "All the former voicemail companies are becoming unified messaging companies," says Ovum's leading analyst David Bradshaw. "We expect in the not too distant future that there will be very little difference in price between unified messaging and voicemail.

Ovum says the choice and maturity of solutions will improve, so there's no rush, unless you are dissatisfied with your existing systems. But if you decide not to go unified now, do not invest in any messaging system without an eye to the future – ensure that the system can be unified. The one problem current unified messaging systems don't solve is so-called "message overload", Bradshaw says. "The next stage is to have smart tools that do automatic message handling: for example, automatically deleting junk mail, or sorting messages into appropriate folders."

AUDIO AND VIDEOCONFERENCING

All you need for audioconferencing is a phone. Suppliers of teleconferencing services will contact the people you wish to talk to, confirm an appropriate time, and then ring them to link them into the audioconference. They will even chair the meetings, and provide tapes and transcripts in hard copy or word-processed form. Alternatively, you can set up the conference yourself. You will be given a phone number which everyone must dial, and a pin number for identification and security purposes.

Audioconferences can also be set up over the internet, via the service provider's website. Not long from now, all the work of setting up the call will by done by intelligent agents, pieces of software residing on the network. It is already possible to set up audioconferences via e-mail products that check everyone's electronic diary for a suitable slot, then use the e-mail directory to send details and confirmations to all the participants.

Using internet-enabled PCs, it is possible to share screens of data, slides and documents while the conference is going on. Participants can even manipulate the data, and send one another confidential messages. Soon, the boundary between audio-conferences and videoconferences will begin to blur.

Users will be able to see schematic figures representing the participants, and also view 3D representations of objects. Over the last decade, videoconferencing has evolved from an expensive boardroom luxury to one that has the potential to become ubiquitous. Add a cheap video-camera from a high street retailer to a multi-media PC, and you have an instant videoconferencing terminal. As prices have plummeted, image quality has improved, and the old problem of insufficient bandwidth has faded away.

You can install your own videoconferencing equipment and manage it yourself, or use a service provider, that will offer much the same services as for audioconferencing. You can buy a package containing all you need to set up a videoconferencing facility, or simply buy a software package to install on an existing PC. As with audioconferencing, you can also view screens of data, spreadsheets or slides while the conference is going on.

Videoconferences tend to involve smaller numbers of partici-pants than audioconferences. More people means the screen needs to be divided into smaller and smaller windows. Hybrid video/audio conferences can be set up, in which a limited number of people give visual presentations, and a larger number have the opportunity to question them over the phone – rather like a television phone-in.

PBXS AND ACDS

The traditional private branch exchange (PBX) is a switch which handles the call traffic between an organisation's internal lines and the outside world. Increasingly, PBXs are converging with ACDs (automatic call distributors) which are switches designed for call-centre operations. The emergence of switches based on PCs has dramatically cut the cost of both kinds of switches.

Some products have been specifically designed for small and medium-sized businesses and offer even more functionality. They may combine voice telephony with local and wide area networking, unified messaging and internet access.

The drawback is that PCs offer limited growth. "The more you stuff into a PC, the smaller the number of people you can serve from it," says Ovum analyst David Bradshaw. "If you want more than 100 people in your call centre, we recommend that having a high capability switch, or something dedicated like an ACD. You can buy a Lucent switch with an add-on box that runs the ACD software. That is the way the market's heading."

FUTURE FLEXIBILITY

Almost all the products and services described use IP (internet protocol). In fact, the convergence of data and voice on a single network is becoming synonymous with IP. Some organisations will no doubt invest in IP on a single network to cut their costs and simplify network management.

However, this is to ignore the sheer richness of applications that convergence makes possible: the ability to combine audio and video, data, graphics, slides and documents and internet services in any way you like, so as to maximise the effectiveness of your communications, whether with customers or colleagues.

Chapter 9

Strategies for competitive advantage

Companies that win in the information and communications age will be those that have mapped their long-term objectives. David Jackson, director of voice services at Cable & Wireless Communications, looks at how good business plans are born

In theory, the brave new world of convergence promised by the telecoms companies is just around the corner. Cable & Wireless Communications (CWC), for example, is rolling out a £400m service in the UK that should be running by May this year. Based on internet protocol (IP), it will carry many different types of traffic, including multimedia, voice, data and video.

The financial implications are startling. Typically, a 13:1 reduction in start-up costs is being seen for building new systems to replace non-IP services. Within five years, this is expected to improve to between 50 and 100 to one.

Perhaps even more exciting is what convergence means for the way businesses work. Over the next 12-18 months, CWC and its customers will be able to have any service, any "desk", any environment, any sales channel, anywhere.

In practice, though, convergence will only be as good as those who buy and use it. Like all technologies, it should deliver business strategy, not dictate it. Companies have to understand where they are now and where they want to be. They can then use technology to help them move between the two positions safely and profitably.

QUESTIONS FOR BUSINESS

Throughout UK industry, the same basic questions apply. The leaders of multinational companies, large corporations, small and medium-sized enterprises must ask:

- *What are we good at?*

- *What should we be doing in five years' time?*

- *How do we get to where we want to be?*

- *How should we be dealing with customers?*

Always important for businesses, these issues have become more critical with the rise of internet technology. For many companies, the worldwide web has created a turbulent marketplace in which new entrants seem to have instant power to threaten or overturn long-established brands.

CUSTOMER EXPECTATIONS

To keep up in the e-business world, older companies must find a way of capitalising on their infrastructure and their assets, both in terms of money, customers and information. "Cosmetic" or "shop-front" changes are not enough to sustain progress in the face of higher customer expectations and new forms of competition. Indeed, if a company neglects to align the processes needed to fulfill e-commerce orders, it will only turn customers off. A new shop front, therefore, must be accompanied by fundamental changes to processes and systems.

Many companies fail to get the best return on their investment in new technologies. They don't join the e-business community; they just sit at its perimeter. The story is told, for example, of a mortgage company that claimed to do a lot of business on the internet but failed to introduce an automated processing system to back up the new business stream. Printing requests off, tagging them, then taking them down to a processing department as normal is hardly likely to win competitive advantage. For this company, setting up a web site was a cosmetic not a strategic change.

MAKING A PLAN

Building an effective strategy requires an understanding of:

■ *The market and your brand;*

■ *Your customers;*

■ *Your people;*

■ *Systems and technology.*

Establish how the market you operate in actually works. Companies need to ask themselves what they are good at and where they really make money. The answers are not always obvious. A home shopping company, for example, makes its money not from selling products and services over a telephone line but from being a finance house, from credit and hire purchase agreements.

You must also know what your customers think of you. Misunderstanding your relationship with your customers is one of the most dangerous mistakes you can make. Coca-Cola's launch of the New Coke formula in the 1980s was a marketing disaster because the company had failed to understand the value people placed on the original drink. And the current problems of Marks & Spencer could be blamed partly on a failure to appreciate the wants and needs of core, older customers.

CUSTOMERS, COMPETITORS AND STAFF

Find out what actually sells the product. Is it the brand, the products and services themselves, the convenience of the channel that you sell through, some or all of the above?

When you have found out what customers think of you now, look at what you are planning to do in the future and see how that fits. And consider how it works with your marketplace, your competitors and new entrants.

Find out about your customers and their buying patterns. Who are they? Who do you want them to be? How do you want to be dealing with them? Look at the values and brand image you want to be associated with before you rush into designing a web site.

Look at your people. They need to have the right skills and your company needs to make sure they are "equipped" for the brave new world. Your culture and marketing position may currently be very different from what you want to achieve: how can you make sure your staff will make the transition effectively? You probably won't be able to go to the marketplace to buy new skills because they're expensive and scarce. So look at alternatives such as partnering, even with those that have traditionally been your competitors. Together you might make a killing.

Think also about diversification. Look at the example of Tesco: it has successfully repositioned itself as a quality retailer and now works on the basis that it can sell anything – clothing, pushchairs, mobile phones – so what's to stop you?

OLD AND NEW TECHNOLOGY

Finally, look at your business systems. Most companies have a lot of "legacy" systems – order processing systems, stock control systems, planning systems and so on. Are you going to leave these alone to do what they are good at (running your business)? Or do you want to start building a new raft of integrated information systems, following a convergence path immediately?

Look at the technology to see how it can help you achieve your business objectives and develop and expand your business. Try to do what's best, not what's cheapest or easiest. If you can conceive a way of linking two information systems for business reasons, the chances are it can and will be done.

The features that converged systems offer will mean better service, in a better business. The home shopper should be able to order by e-mail, or telephone or online. You will need to make sure that there is synergy between all channels: it should be possible for somebody making initial contact via the web to be automatically transferred to a live agent, together with the details of what he is doing now and what he has done previously.

Really clever things are still to come. Software houses have started to build intelligent question and answer databases and "smart" front-ends to help sales people. If sales people get stuck they can use e-mail or online chat, or perhaps get help using a voice conversation – at all times being able to share what they have been doing and what they are trying to do.

DO THE BASICS

New converged services will serve the whole spectrum of businesses: a large company may want substantial integration with existing infrastructure; a smaller company might value speed to enter a new market with an innovative service.

But before taking advantage of them, all companies must do the basics. Ask those hard questions. Establish where you are now. Understand your market. And decide where you want to be. And above all, be honest in your answers: if you're not, you'll just be building on sand.

Building the future of Internet communications.

Business Made Simpler

CABLE & WIRELESS

Chapter 10

All for one, one for all

Philip Hunter, technology writer, looks at how three organisations from different sectors have successfully integrated voice/data technologies

TALK IS CHEAPER

Supplier of industrial gases Linde Gas decided to use internet protocol (IP) for voice transmission because of the cost savings involved. "The interest was to get voice and fax for free by putting that on the same lines as the data and so avoiding all telephone charges," says Simon Brown, sales director of Scalable Networks, the company that installed the voice over internet protocol (VoIP) system for Linde Gas. The system connects six regional sites with each other and with Linde Gas's headquarters in West Bromwich, providing four voice channels as well as data transmission capacity.

The installation could be called second generation: it allows the local private branch exchange (PBX) telephone systems to be connected directly to the routers used to control the flow of data through the network.

Linde Gas was an early convert to voice/data integration, having routed voice over data links before turning to Scalable Networks for a more advanced solution. With the old first-generation system, the voice and data had to be integrated via a separate hardware box, called a multiplexer, before being connected to the wide area IP network.

The new system is more resilient as well as being cheaper to run: Scalable Networks has installed dial-up ISDN circuits to back up permanent kilostream leased lines interconnecting the sites. The ISDN connections provide the same bandwidth, 64kbps, as the permanent circuits, and cut in automatically in the event of a line failure. As a result, users are not affected when faults occur.

Although not as good as that transmitted over conventional telephone systems, the voice quality has proved adequate. The fact that the number of voice channels has been limited to four at least ensures that quality is consistent. Squeezing in more voice channels would stretch the capacity of the system (quality would suffer when all channels were in use) and leave insufficient room for data.

The fact that the IP protocol provides the option of prioritising voice over data also helps maintain quality standards. Voice conversations are "protected" from data activities, in effect giving them a dedicated slice of the overall transmission circuit. Most VoIP installations take advantage of this option: data applications such as e-mail cannot – unlike communications by voice – be ruined by a few seconds' delay.

As data becomes increasingly important to a company, however, performance becomes an issue. Pressure on transmission bandwidth when voice communications are taking place has caused some of Linde Gas's software applications to slow down. To ease the bottleneck, the company is doubling the capacity of its circuits to 128kbps.

So the voice is not completely free. It is free of dial-up telephone charges, but there is a knock on effect on the amount of capacity needed for data. This is a point to bear in mind when listening to the pitches of VoIP vendors.

It's also important to recognise, however, that VoIP brings benefits beyond cost savings. For Linde Gas it has enabled the whole phone network to operate as if it were connected to a single PBX.

This means that functions such as call divert and short code dialling can automatically be used across the whole enterprise, which is not always possible when each site has its own local telephone network based on a local exchange.

FORCE TO BE RECKONED WITH

The squeeze on defence spending means the RAF has to show that any IT project will deliver measurable returns on investment in a short time. The help desk team based at RAF Wyton in Huntingdon, Cambridgeshire has gone one step further, proving that effective deployment of IT actually reduces costs.

Like many organisations, the RAF relies increasingly on help desks to support users. Any move to cut costs and reduce manning levels, must not, therefore, be at the expense of service.

The RAF's solution was to introduce an interactive voice response (IVR) system that both "answers" simple queries and helps agents deal with more difficult problems quickly and effectively.

The IVR solution combines the existing help desk system, the Redbox Service Management System from Ultracomp, with a new Phonexus computer telephony system from IVS, a provider of integrated computing/voice systems.

IVR gathers as much information as possible about the caller and the problem and presents it to the agent as soon as the call is handed over. The agent does not have to waste time asking routine questions and can proceed straight to the heart of the problem. (The time spent by agents on an average call has been cut by almost two minutes.)

Callers identify themselves to the help desk by entering their own extension number by direct dial input (DDI). The IVR system provides "caller screening", distinguishing between people ringing to report a problem for the first time and those ringing for an update on progress. The latter are asked for a log number, which is then transmitted to the help desk system. The case details are obtained and forwarded to the agent taking the call.

Calling line identifier (CLI), an alternative way of identifying callers, was rejected by the RAF since it does not always work for overseas users.

The RAF system is a classic application of CTI (computer telephony integration), with the core ingredients being CTI boards from Brooktrout Technology. These boards handle the IVR message playback in response to the caller's actions.

In the event of a widespread RAF technical fault, when the help desk can be overloaded, recorded messages inform users of progress. "The IVR system enables us to record information for callers in the event of a large rush of calls," says Bob Coe, the RAF help desk manager.

The new technology has enabled a small team of agents to deal with more than 2,500 detailed calls a month. "We generally have a maximum of four help desk operators available at any one time for a user base of 3,500 people, and the ability to offer information via the automated system has proved invaluable in making best use of manpower," says Coe.

As well as minimising the number of agents needed to support the user base, the IVR system has reduced the number of calls lost, particularly at peak times. This in turn increases satisfaction with the system, and improves overall efficiency because users spend less time on the phone.

BOX OF TRICKS

One of the biggest potential applications for voice/data integration is unified messaging: notification of e-mail, telephone and fax messages from one "mailbox".

The European mobile telephone operator Optimus asked the office system vendor Intersis to install a unified messaging system for its 650 employees, who are dispersed across five sites. Optimus wanted a fax and voice mail system that was compatible with its existing system for e-mail. "Each site had its own MS-Exchange server for e-mail forming part of a single network and it was essential that any messaging solution considered should be capable of integrating fully with this environment," says Rui Paiva, the Optimus manager of management information systems.

Now staff have a single mailbox within MS-Exchange, which they can access from a desktop PC, using standard Exchange client software such as Outlook 97. All messages are highlighted on a single screen, allowing users to read or print them if they are faxes or e-mails, or to listen to them over their telephone extensions if they are voice mails. Voice messages can also be accessed from other office extensions and from external phones and mobiles. There is also the possibility of converting e-mails into voice messages for remote playback over phones. Optimus has kept traditional private branch exchanges at each of its sites, partly because it is not yet possible to provide the full range of calling, diversion and messaging features over a pure internet protocol network. Integration in this case is at the application rather than network communication level.

In fact each of the five sites has a Nortel Meridien PABX with two basic rate ISDN lines, and four analogue lines connected to a voice server, which provides the unified messaging capability. This server is in turn connected to a fax server and a Microsoft Exchange server at each site. The recording and playback of voice messages, and indeed the whole unified messaging, is controlled by computer telephony boards made by Brooktrout Technology.

These boards provide functions such as DTMF tone detection, allowing callers to control the recording and playback of messages. The boards also ensure that voice messages are played back at the correct speed and tone.

The adoption of unified messaging has led to a significant change in working practice, and as well as saving time has improved communications among the 650 Optimus staff, all of whom now use their PCs to manage all inbound and outbound messaging. An interesting side effect is that the system has increased use of voice messaging as an alternative to e-mail or fax in some situations. Voice messaging has the advantage that emphasis, urgency, and emotion as well as mere words can be conveyed, thereby transmitting more information. So now that sending voice messages is as easy as fax or e-mail, the appropriate medium for each task can be used.

Sponsor a Director's Guide

With more than 50 titles produced, the Director's Guide series is a highly successful business publishing venture

Each guide is produced in conjunction with a major blue-chip sponsor – from Oracle and Grant Thornton to Cable & Wireless and Fedex – and each is sent free to 50,000 individual members of the IoD in the UK.

Director's Guides cover a diverse range of topics – from e-commerce to growth finance, from customer care to management buy-outs. Research shows the series forms a key part of IoD members' business reading, with a high retention value and pass-on readership. The direct benefits to the sponsor include:

- *50,000 individual director-level circulation*
- *Strong position as an authority in its specialist area*
- *Authorship of three chapters*
- *Full co-branding with the IoD*
- *Seven pages of exclusive advertising, including two colour positions on the covers*
- *A reply-paid card bound into the guide, for direct response*
- *3,000 sponsor copies*
- *Broad press coverage*

For further enquiries, please contact
Business Development and Sponsorship on:
020 7766 8885
or e-mail us at busdev@iod.co.uk

Chapter 11

Choosing a service provider

Outsourcing can help make sense of convergence and be a cost-effective alternative to an in-house IT team. But how do you find the right support agency for you? Annie Gurton, technology writer, offers some pointers

Only a really large company with its own experienced in-house teams dedicated to IT, telecoms and marketing could possibly manage the development, implementation and long-term support of its converging network and applications.

Most businesses about to enter the convergence age face three choices:

- *To start hiring the highly skilled, experienced and, therefore, expensive staff;*

- *To find, brief and manage a different external IT services provider for each of the different aspects of the network;*

- *To use a single professional support organisation that can take complete end-to-end responsibility of all the services that are required.*

For simplicity and cost reasons, the last is usually the best option.

EARLY STAGES OF SELECTION

But how do you go about selecting that all-singing, all-dancing professional support organisations? Competence, experience, cost and flexibility should be your primary considerations. You need an organisation that is going to work in partnership with you and that understands your market – your competitors and business pressures as well as your opportunities and your goals.

Although company networks tend to rely on the same fundamental technology, they are set up and configured in different ways, using the hardware and software and the products thought to meet the needs of a business and its processes best.

Businesses in the retail sector, for example, often have an extremely high number of brands. They need an underlying network that can capture data from a variety of sources – and warehouse it and analyse it – and allow for the rapid delivery of management reports to the right decision makers. They have a vital need for network storage and for technological infrastructure that can cope with high volumes of data flowing from points of sale to purchasing departments and warehouses.

Manufacturing companies, by contrast, usually have to deal with fewer documents and files, flowing in more structured directions. These documents and files will be big, and the data in them will need to be archived. Access times and response times, however, will probably not need to be so fast.

The first stage, therefore, is to identify a network support company that understands your sector and your business. The second is to make sure that there will be shared responsibility for the efficiency and smooth-running of the network.

The next is to work out the terms and service level agreement (SLA) that you expect to be working to, ensuring that the third party does not have a different vision of the way the relationship will work.

CULTURE AND CREDENTIALS

Once appointed, the networking support and service agency should take a proactive project-management approach. Timescales, goals and contingency plans need to be agreed, channels of communication need to be clearly defined, and regular meetings need to be held.

For a networking support company to succeed, therefore, its interpersonal skills need to be as good as its technical skills. You should bear this in mind when making your decision: be assured from the outset that the company is adopting the right approach and is committed to your organisation.

You – and the relevant members of your staff – must be able to get on with the third party. Its consultants will work alongside your managers, listening to your needs and expectations, but also advising in the light of their experience. They need to be able to develop informal but effective relationships and be able to explain and share a common vision. Building and developing a converged network is a difficult process and needs to be based on a shared strategy that is clearly understood and communicated. If the agency has a culture that differs dramatically from yours such understanding is unlikely to develop.

The design of networks, especially those that are required to carry both voice and data, is highly complex. Issues such as testing, load balancing, integration of legacy systems (so that historical investment is not wasted), data integrity and security all need to be considered. It is therefore essential that all the technical staff involved with your project are trained to recognised standards and have the appropriate qualifications. Certified Novell Engineers (CNEs), Cisco Certified Internetworking Expert (CCIEs) and those with Microsoft qualifications are among safe bets.

THE DANGER OF THE SPECIALIST

Another thing to look out for is inclusivity. Some third parties are only really able to deal with a limited number of types of network or vendor product. They may claim that they know all types of network and can guarantee inter-operability, but in fact their knowledge may be restricted to a few mainstream brands and protocols. This could be a very significant and serious problem when you come to inter-operate with other firms. If your network is unable to communicate with all possible external networks or protocols, you will hit trouble when you start to do business over it. Don't, therefore, just look for mainstream accreditation: ensure your services provider has experience of all kinds of technical solutions.

Paper qualifications also need to be backed up with practical experience, and you should ensure that the third party can provide independent references from a selection of the clients it has worked with on leading-edge networking solutions. Ideally, look for a satisfied client in your own sector to be doubly sure that the provider understands your business needs.

Be suspicious of providers that don't seem to use the latest technological aides in running the project – or in managing their contract with you. All high-flying project managers today use the internet, and you should be offered an intranet link early in the relationship. This will allow you to contact your support engineers and receive prompt answers to any queries, in a confidential, secure environment. An intranet should also be used to disseminate documentation, saving time and cost in distribution.

THE BENEFITS OF BESPOKE SERVICE

You should be offered a choice between different levels of implementation and support – and therefore different price ranges. If you have some expertise in-house, your staff should work with the third party in a complementary way, thus avoiding duplication of the work being done by the external team reducing costs.

The third party should be flexible enough to use your staff when appropriate, working with them and supporting them, covering any gaps in their knowledge. In a converged environment, it is often difficult for in-house telecoms staff to understand a data network and vice versa, and a suitable third party will identify your weaknesses and where skills need to be supplemented.

Different businesses have different support needs. Some organisations, for example, only need help at the design and implementation phases and are confident that their in-house staff can cope with the long-term user and system support. Others prefer the comfort of knowing that they have a team of support engineers always available at all times. Again, if the third party has the appropriate flexibility, the agreement can be tailored to your specific needs and situation.

It may also be best for you to use a third party solely for networking the desktops, retaining control of the server or mainframe networking yourself. There can be considerable cost and efficiency benefits to outsourcing desktop network management.

Many surveys that look at Cost of Ownership (COI) and Return on Investment (ROI) issues conclude that using a third party for desktop network management delivers high savings and improved efficiency.

COLLABORATION NOT CONTROL

Whatever kind of contract and SLA you decide on, you will want to be sure that the tail won't wag the dog. As the relationship develops, some third-party support organisations seem to forget that you are the client and take a dictatorial approach to the relationship. While they are the experts and their views and expertise should undoubtedly be respected, they should also work closely with your staff to ensure that your views are listened to and objectives met.

Positive management of the relationship with the third party is essential. It should be the specific responsibility of at least one in-house individual, who will ensure your needs are met. A single point of contact from your side should have a single point of contact within the third party.

You will want, in the relationship, to consider and anticipate future needs as well as satisfy current ones. The third party should be pro-active about recommending how your network and IT should evolve and develop. Although you can - and should - keep an eye on new technological developments yourself, judging whether the time is right for your business to review its systems, the third party, with its broad collection of consultants and expert technicians and its close relationships with equipment makers, should be well placed to give good advice. Its recommendations should reflect an understanding of your business and market.

VALUE-FOR-MONEY VISION

Essentially, you need a third party with vision. Networking is a fast-evolving, highly complex technology, and although there are tools and techniques to make it easier, the ability to understand the basics, assess the value in innovations and see where they can be integrated into existing environments remains essential.

There still needs to be a fundamental understanding of how networking and converged environments can be used for individual business advantage.

The word partnership is now somewhat hackneyed, but it describes well the kind of relationship that should exist between you and the networking implementation and support agency. You need to be able to view it as an extension of your own business, talking in confidence about business threats, pressures and competition, as well as the new products you want to develop and the opportunities that you want to take. Without that level of trust and confidence, the third party will be unable to deliver the network you need – one that will truly integrate voice, data and other media in the future to your competitive advantage.

Of course, none of this comes cheaply. In the selection process, price is undoubtedly an issue, but the old maxim about peanuts and monkeys applies. If a third party makes a proposition that seriously undercuts the others, view it with scepticism. High-level skills and experience are expensive. If you baulk at the cost of third parties consider this: could you afford to pay the salaries of the highly-skilled and experienced people they employ?